SB
951.4
D53

First American Edition

Chemical Publishing Co Inc
New York NY

ISBN HMSO 0 11 240872 9

ISBN Chemical Publishing Co Inc 0 8206 0294 9

FOREWORD

This book is published as an aid to the diagnosis of herbicide injury to crops. Many herbicides are used in agriculture and horticulture so instances of crop damage from accidental overdosing and other causes may occasionally occur. When determining whether herbicide damage has occurred a knowledge of the type of symptoms to be expected and an understanding of the behaviour of the herbicide are essential. The book includes illustrations of damage to crops caused by examples of the main groups of herbicides and a detailed explanation of the factors involved when injury occurs.

The publication was prepared by Mr D J Eagle, Specialist in Pesticide Residues, ADAS, Cambridge and Dr D J Caverly, Analytical Chemist, ADAS, Wye with assistance from Dr K Holly, Weed Research Organisation, Oxford. Most of the colour plates were prepared by ADAS. There are also some plates from the Weed Research Organisation and the National Vegetable Research Station and these are gratefully acknowledged.

W Dermott
Head of the Agricultural
Science Service

CONTENTS

INTRODUCTION

This publication is a guide to the recognition of symptoms of damage caused by herbicides to crop plants, the factors affecting their occurrence and the risks of confusion with similar symptoms not caused by herbicides. During the last two decades there has been a rapid increase in the use of agricultural and horticultural pesticides especially of herbicides for weed control. Consequently there are more opportunities for accidental mis-application leading to damaged crops. New herbicides have been developed with selectivity between closely related species such as control of grass weeds in cereals, and the margin of error for giving adequate weed control without crop damage is sometimes small. It is impracticable to include illustrations of all herbicides and all crops but sufficient are included to show the type of damage caused by the major groups of herbicides.

Diagnosis of herbicide damage and the reasons for its occurrence requires a knowledge of the symptoms produced by the herbicide or herbicides involved and of their persistence, movement in soils and their availability to plants. Incorrect usage of chemicals can lead to serious loss of crop; when damage occurs it is important to determine which herbicide was involved and why.

Diagnosis of herbicide damage and attribution of responsibility is rarely straightforward. When a case of suspected herbicide damage occurs it is generally advisable to inform and liaise with the manufacturer or supplier.

WAYS IN WHICH HERBICIDE DAMAGE MAY OCCUR

OVERDOSING

Crops can be accidentally overdosed with herbicide in a variety of ways. It can be on a field scale by simply making an error and applying the wrong rate, but more commonly damage is in patches. The most common type of overdosing is due to double dosing where spray booms overlap. Damage can then occur in narrow strips across the field approximately a boom width apart or on headland areas which are double-dosed while the sprayer is turning.

Over-application due to defective nozzles is another type of overdosing which gives a regular pattern of damage in each spray bout depending on the position in the boom of the faulty nozzle or nozzles. Faulty spray equipment leading to uneven pressure along the boom can result in underdosing at the ends of the boom and overdosing from the middle. Again, a recognisable pattern can be detected.

Inefficient mixing of water and herbicide can cause uneven application resulting first in overdosing and then underdosing as the tank empties. Fluctuating tractor speeds on a gradient can produce a banded pattern of damage across the field.

Many soil acting herbicides e.g. simazine and lenacil require a small dose on light soils and a larger dose on heavy ones. An incorrect assessment of the texture can lead to overdosing. It is quite common for fields to contain soils of contrasting texture leading to overdosing of lighter patches. Gravelly areas in light sandy fields are particularly prone to such overdosing because most soil acting herbicides are unsafe on very gravelly soils.

The pattern of occurrence is an important diagnostic criterion. If some such pattern cannot be detected in the occurrence of the symptoms believed to be due to herbicide damage then the problem is unlikely to have been caused by a herbicide. Small areas apparently missed by the spray can often be a very helpful clue.

CONTAMINATION

Spray equipment is used for a variety of chemicals on most farms including nutrients, insecticides and fungicides, as well as herbicides. Some crops are extremely sensitive to small amounts of herbicide; if the equipment is not thoroughly cleaned after use the next crop to be sprayed may be damaged. Many crops, particularly horticultural crops such as lettuce, tomatoes and cucumbers, are very sensitive to traces of growth regulator (hormone) herbicide and may be damaged if cleaning has been inadequate. Contamination of the spray lance or tank will often cause symptoms of decreasing severity as spraying proceeds and tanks are refilled.

Contamination of spray materials sometimes occurs, for example, by accidentally topping up a partly filled can with another containing a different chemical.

Contaminated water has occasionally caused problems when spray tanks have been filled from water in ponds or ditches previously contaminated with discarded cans of herbicide. Drainage dykes are sometimes sprayed with herbicides for weed control and are a possible hazard if water is extracted for irrigation. By the time the symptoms of damage become obvious analysis of water or plant material may show no trace of toxicant. In streams and moving waterways soluble herbicides are rapidly flushed although samples of mud may still contain measurable residues several months after contamination.

SPRAY OR VAPOUR DRIFT

These problems occur when spray or vapour of herbicide drifts on to sensitive neighbouring crops. Droplets of paraquat or diquat can drift for several hundred metres under windy conditions, causing small areas of necrosis and chlorosis to leaf tissue. Convection can cause movement of droplets in very still conditions. When spraying near a sensitive crop it is safest when a gentle breeze is blowing away from it.

Vapour drift, especially of volatile ester formulations of growth regulator herbicides, can drift, to cause damage to sensitive crops e.g. tomatoes or cucumbers. Dichlobenil vapour can drift under warm dry conditions causing damage especially to sensitive glasshouse crops and for this reason its use close to buildings is not recommended.

ADSORPTION AND LEACHING

The successful use of most soil-acting herbicides and avoidance of crop damage depends on the development of a good root system below the concentration of herbicide in the uppermost part of the soil. Crop damage will occur if downward root development is restricted by soil compaction just below sowing depth resulting in a concentration of roots near the surface and excessive uptake of the herbicide. Shallow drilling of seed into the concentrated zone can also result in excessive uptake and damage. Conversely, excessively deep drilling can result in damage from some triazine herbicides, notably terbutryne, due to uptake through the shoot.

The movement of herbicides in soils is complex. Most soil-acting materials are of low water solubility and are strongly adsorbed by soils thus remaining close to the soil surface. An exception is isocarbamid which is moderately soluble, does not adsorb and leaches readily. The degree of adsorption is a factor mainly of organic matter content and clay fraction. In spite of these two properties movement does occur if heavy rains follow application before chemical equilibrium has been established or, by the flow of microparticles with adsorbed herbicide through fissures in the soil.

The most soluble herbicides bear electrical charges and can be separated into two groups. Those positively charged e.g. paraquat, diquat and glyphosate are very strongly adsorbed to the negative adsorption sites on the clay particles and therefore move very little in solution once equilibrium has been established. The negatively charged group includes TBA, dicamba, TCA, dalapon and the phenoxy acid hormones (not esters) which are readily leached in soils under heavy rainfall. Movement of herbicides to lower zones can be reversed as the upper layer of soil dries, causing upward movement of water.

SOIL RESIDUES

Some of the more persistent soil-acting herbicides remain active in the soil for many months. The manufacturers of such herbicides stipulate minimum periods which must elapse before a succeeding crop can be grown and in some cases ploughing, rather than direct drilling or tined cultivations, is also required. Damage to a following crop is possible if any one of these directions is not followed. Even when the requirements are met, damage may be encountered in areas which have been seriously overdosed. In exceptionally dry seasons even moderately persistent herbicides may persist beyond the usual safe period and affect the next crop.

A recognisable pattern of injury by herbicide residues can usually be discerned in crops. Damage is always most severe in areas where spray booms have overlapped and on headlands where the sprayer has turned. If the herbicide was applied to potatoes there may be strips of damaged crop corresponding to the bottom of each ridge.

If most of the crop is affected it is usually possible to find undamaged areas which have been missed by the spray.

TRASH RESIDUES

Emerging seedlings can be damaged by paraquat remaining on trash following a pre-emergence application of paraquat.

APPLICATION AT THE WRONG GROWTH STAGE

Application of many herbicides is recommended within precisely defined stages of the crop's development. Growth regulators (hormones) for weed control in winter cereals generally have to be applied after the fully tillered stage but before the first node or 'joint' can be seen or felt on the stem. Application too early can cause deformation of ears and application too late can give shrivelled grain or cause ears to be partially blind. Several crops can be damaged by applying post-emergence herbicides at the early seedling stage before proper establishment. Late application of paraquat for pre-emergence weed control can result in yellow chlorosis to the leaf tips of emerging seedlings.

CAUSES OF CONFUSION IN SYMPTOM RECOGNITION

SIMILARITY OF SYMPTOMS WITHIN HERBICIDE GROUPS

Herbicides in a particular group, for example the triazines, the substituted ureas or the uracils, all give symptoms of damage very similar to other herbicides in the same group. On the basis of symptoms alone it would be impossible to distinguish between, for example, the triazines, simazine and terbutryne or the substituted ureas linuron and metoxuron.

Although there are recognisable differences between symptoms caused by different growth regulators (hormones) it is in practice very difficult to decide which herbicide is involved on the basis of the symptoms alone because of similarities between the symptoms produced. Also the range of symptom expression from slight to severe is very wide. So, particularly as many herbicides of this type are mixtures of growth regulators, the symptoms are rarely specific enough to pinpoint any one product. An exception to this is the distortions, produced by the foliar action of dicamba, which are commonly accompanied by yellow areas on the leaf.

SIMILARITY OF SYMPTOMS BETWEEN HERBICIDE GROUPS

Some quite different groups of herbicides give rather similar symptoms. The substituted ureas and uracils both cause yellowing (chlorosis) along the veins, in broad leaved crops, which later turn brown (necrotic). Chlorosis of the veins can also occur by uptake of chlorate residues. In cereals the symptoms caused by triazines, substituted ureas and uracils are all very similar when in a moderately advanced stage. Although chlorosis caused by substituted ureas and uracils tends to start in the middle of the leaf it rapidly becomes bleached and extends towards the tip of the leaves and so resembles the symptoms of triazine damage which start at the tip.

SIMILARITY BETWEEN SYMPTOMS CAUSED BY HERBICIDES AND OTHER PESTICIDES

Damage to cereals from soil residues of propyzamide or carbetamide is expressed as stunting and thickening of the coleoptile and stunting of roots with thickening of the tips. These symptoms are indistinguishable from damage caused by excessive organo-mercury seed treatment or by accidental contamination of the seed with the sprout suppressant chlorpropham (CIPC). Other herbicides such as dichlobenil and trifluralin also cause stunting and thickening of roots.

RANGE OF SYMPTOMS PRODUCED BY A HERBICIDE

The symptoms of damage by a herbicide to a particular crop vary considerably with the dose. Crops slightly affected by substituted ureas, for example, show slight veinal chlorosis with little retardation in growth. As the dose increases the chlorosis becomes more extensive and turns necrotic. The necrosis extends first along the veins but with increasing severity progressively affects the whole leaf and eventually results in plant death. So substituted urea damage to a crop cannot be fully represented by a single photograph. However, in any case of herbicide damage there is usually a range of symptom expression which includes plants with recognisable symptoms typical of the herbicide involved.

SIMILARITY OF SYMPTOMS BETWEEN HERBICIDES AND OTHER CAUSES

Bleaching of the leaf tips of cereal plants can occur due to the presence of triazine, substituted urea or uracil residues. This normally starts at the leaf tips and spreads, usually under conditions of rapid growth, to affect the whole plant. When not severe this can closely resemble potash deficiency, frost damage and scorch from a foliage-acting herbicide or liquid fertiliser. Other evidence such as the pattern of distribution and weather must always be taken into account when diagnosing problems. Drought can cause severe leaf scorch which may resemble herbicide symptoms in some crops. Wind damage can cause leaf tipping which is similar to scorch caused by foliar sprays. Plant tissue damaged by chemical or physical agents will allow freer access to pathogens and viruses which may then show as a secondary cause of damage.

DIFFICULTIES IN OBTAINING A DEFINITE DIAGNOSIS

Modern agriculture and horticulture makes use of so many chemicals and techniques that it is frequently very difficult to ascribe symptoms to any one cause. For example the soil may have been treated with a nematicide or fumigant before sowing followed by pre-emergence and post-emergence herbicides and there may have been a risk of herbicide residues from the previous crop. If damage to such a crop is not investigated until some weeks after it occurs it may be impossible to ascertain the cause, particularly if the damaged plants have subsequently died with no recognisable symptoms. If the damage had been caused by herbicide residues the delay before examination may have resulted in disappearance of the residues.

EFFECTS OF SOIL AND WEATHER CONDITIONS

Interaction with soil conditions is frequently a factor in the occurrence of herbicide damage. If soil compaction below drilling depth confines the roots of seedlings to the surface with maximum herbicide concentration then too much herbicide is taken up. This type of injury is most likely when growth is poor due to wet conditions resulting in partially anaerobic conditions in the compacted layer, which are unsuitable for root growth. Small seeded crops such as onions can fail under such conditions even without the application of a herbicide so it is sometimes virtually impossible to determine whether to blame the herbicide or the seedbed preparation. In favourable weather the crop may have made more vigorous root growth and avoided damage. However, the occurrence of exceptionally warm weather soon after application of a pre-emergence soil-acting herbicide can lead to rapid growth and uptake of herbicides with consequent crop damage.

Crops suffering from stress due to drought or the effects of a pathogen or pest on the roots are more likely to succumb to soil residues than healthy crops. A well-known example of herbicide damage occurring only when application is under drought conditions is the vascular browning and rotting whcih can occur in potato tubers after the haulm is 'burned off' with diquat or dinoseb.

Plants affected by early frosts are more susceptible to foliage-applied herbicides although moderately low temperatures may induce dormancy making them more tolerant.

Prolonged water stress can result in thickening of the cuticle and increased pubescence producing less penetration of herbicide. Damage to the cuticle by wind or other agents e.g. soil residues of TCA will increase the plant's susceptibility to foliage-applied herbicides; because of this rates of post-emergent herbicides e.g. dinoseb are reduced where previous sprays of aliphatic chlorinated herbicides have been used.

High relative humidity generally leads to a more rapid penetration into the leaves and translocation.

THE ROLE OF ANALYSIS IN DETERMINING THE CAUSE OF CROP DAMAGE

SOIL ANALYSIS

Analyses of soils and/or plants can be helpful in diagnosing and confirming herbicide damage. However, great care must be taken with the sampling if erroneous conclusions are to be avoided. Analyses of the soil are usually most helpful with soil-acting herbicides and usually of no value with foliage-acting herbicides. Soil analysis can be more easily interpreted than plant analysis, which may be subjected to dilution of herbicide within the growing plant; and problems of metabolites are less likely in soils than in plants. Also it is analytically easier because less organic material is removed in the solvent used to extract the herbicide than in the case of plants. Soil samples must be taken to precise depths so that the amount detected on analysis can be related to amount per hectare. Choice of sampling depth depends on type of herbicide, the amount of rainfall since application and whether the soil has been ploughed or cultivated since application. Most soil-acting herbicides are strongly adsorbed and leach down very slowly so it is important to sample the top 5 cm or so for a recently applied herbicide. For a herbicide applied some months previously or before a period of heavy rain two depths for example 0–5 and 5–10 cm or 0–7.5 and 7.5–15 cm are appropriate. If the land has been ploughed or the herbicide is a type which is not adsorbed, for example TCA, (see 'adsorption and leaching' [p.2]) a single sample to plough depth is suitable. As it is always difficult to interpret analyses with any precision and the amount present may have declined since the damage occurred it is always helpful to take comparative samples from a nearby area of normal or better crop. When this is done the sampling depths should be precisely the same as for the affected area.

PLANT ANALYSIS

For foliage-acting herbicides analysis of the plant can occasionally be helpful. Again it is essential to sample both affected and normal areas. The samples should be of whole plants if possible or otherwise of leaves at the same stage of development. Analysis is often not helpful in spray drift incidents involving growth regulators except in cases of severe damage because they are active at such low levels, frequently at about the level of detection, and by the time leaf symptoms have developed most of the parent herbicide will have been converted to metabolites thus making analysis very difficult. Drift of paraquat or paraquat picked up from trash can usually be confirmed analytically unless the damage is slight.

DELAY IN DEVELOPMENT OF SYMPTOMS

Damage caused by spray or vapour drift of 2, 4–D may take several weeks to manifest as typical leaf symptoms. Tomatoes planted into compost containing moderately high residues of TBA (0.01 mg/kg) will take three or four weeks before showing characteristic leaf and growing point symptoms. Seeds of most plants sown into soil containing residues of herbicides causing inhibition of photosynthesis such as the triazines will often show normal germination and early growth until the rate of transpiration reaches a critical level. For cereals damage is often not seen until the spring when rapid transpiration commences.

GROUPS OF HERBICIDES, PROPERTIES AND SYMPTOMS OF DAMAGE

	Common Name	Approved Products
SUBSTITUTED UREAS (Plates 1.1 — 1.8)	chlorbromuron	Maloran
	chloroxuron	Tenoran
	chlortoluron	Dicurane 500L
	diuron *	Hoechst Diuron, Karmex Diuron
	isoproturon	Tolkan, Hytane, Arelon
	linuron *	Afalon, Liquid Linuron, PBI Liquid Linuron, Du Pont Linuron 50 Weedkiller
	methabenzthiazuron	Tribunil
	metoxuron *	Dosaflo, Deftor
	monolinuron	Arresin Emulsion

*Also occurs in mixtures.

The substituted ureas are a large group of soil-acting herbicides ranging in persistence from about a month to over a year. They are inhibitors of photosynthesis and cause chlorosis along the veins which can later turn necrotic (brown in most crops, white in oats and barley) and extend across the veins. The older leaves are generally the worst affected. In cereals chlorosis starts about mid leaf and then extends to the tip.

Examples are given below of crops damaged by residues of herbicide applied to a previous crop.

Herbicide	Crop	Residue in soil mg/kg
chlorbromuron	cabbage	0.43
chlortoluron	turnip	0.34
diuron	grass	0.55
linuron	Brussels sprout	0.38
	lettuce	0.26
metoxuron	oilseed rape	0.24
monolinuron	cabbage	0.40
	leeks	0.20

	Common Name	Approved Products
URACILS (Plates 2.1 — 2.9)	bromacil	Hyvar × Bromacil Weedkiller
	lenacil	Venzar Lenacil Weedkiller
	terbacil	Sinbar Terbacil Weedkiller

The uracils are persistent soil-acting herbicides. Terbacil and bromacil generally persist for more than a year. Lenacil generally persists for less than a year. The uracils are inhibitors of photosynthesis and symptoms of damage are very similar to those due to substituted ureas described in the previous section.

Examples are given below of crops damaged by residues of herbicides applied to a previous crop.

Herbicide	Crop	Residue in soil mg/kg
lenacil	kale	0.08
	carrot	0.16
	wheat	0.09
	lettuce	0.05
terbacil	sugar beet	0.06
	cabbage	0.16

TRIAZINES
(Plates 3.1-3.9)

Common Name	Approved Products
atrazine	Residox, Vectal SC, Gesaprim, Square Deal Atrazine, MSS Atrazine 50, SB Atrazine Flowable
aziprotryne	Brasoran
cyanazine *	Fortrol
desmetryne	Semeron
prometryne	Gesagard, Square Deal Prometryne
simazine *	Boots Simazine 50, Campbell's Simazine, BH Simazine, Murphy Simazine, SB Simazine, MSS Simazine, Simadex, Gesatop, Weedex S2G.
terbuthylazine	Opogard (mixture with terbutryne)
terbutryne *	Clarosan, Prebane 500L
trietazine	Aventox SC, Remtal SC (mixtures with simazine) Bronox (mixture with linuron)

* Also occurs in mixtures

The triazines are a large group of soil-acting herbicides with persistence of about a month to a year. They are inhibitors of photosynthesis like the substituted ureas and uracils but the symptoms of chlorosis and necrosis differ in tending towards the tip and margin of the leaf. The older leaves are generally the worst affected.

Examples of crops damaged by residues from a previous crop are given below.

Herbicide	Crop	Residue in soil mg/kg
atrazine	oats	0.09
	pea	0.09
	wheat	0.23
prometryne	lettuce	0.11
	navy beans	0.22
simazine	cabbage	0.15
	runner beans	0.12
	wheat	0.30

TRIAZINONES
Plates 4.1–4.3

Common Name	Approved Products
metamitron	Goltix
metribuzin	Sencorex

The triazinones are soil-acting inhibitors of photosynthesis and give similar symptoms to the triazines described in the previous section.

Examples of crops damaged by soil residues are given below.

Herbicide	Crop	Residue in soil mg/kg
metribuzin	barley	0.23
	wheat	0.08
	onion	0.08

Ploughing is recommended before growing a susceptible crop after a crop treated with metribuzin.

CHLORIDAZON
(plates 5.1-5.2)

Approved Products

Pyramin, Boots Prybeet, Murphy New Murbetex, Trojan, ABM Pyrazone, Hyzon, MSS Sugar Beet Weedkiller.

Chloridazon is an inhibitor of photosynthesis with both soil and foliage action. Symptoms of damage are similar to those caused by triazines and triazinones described in the previous sections.

AMIDES
(Plates 6.1-6.9)

Common Name	Approved Products	Action
benzoylprop ethyl	Suffix	foliage
carbetamide	Carbetamex	soil
flamprop isopropyl	Barnon	foliage
flamprop methyl	Mataven	foliage
pentanochlor	Herbon Solan	soil
propachlor	Ramrod, Herbon Orange, Hoechst Propachlor, SB Propachlor 65	soil
propyzamide	Kerb	soil
diphenamid	Enid 50W	soil

The amide group includes both soil and foliage-acting herbicides. They are inhibitors of cell division. Grasses and cereals are particularly susceptible to the soil-acting amides which cause stunting and swelling of roots with formation of bulbous tips. Shoot growth is stunted and leaves may be a darker green than in normal plants. In cereals the coleoptiles are stunted and swollen; emergence is delayed or suppressed. Persistence of soil-acting herbicides in this group varies from about a month to about a year. Ploughing is recommended before growing a susceptible crop after a crop treated with propyzamide which is the most persistent of the amides. Examples are given below of crops damaged by residues of a herbicide applied to the previous crop.

Herbicide	Crop	Residue in soil mg/kg
propyzamide	wheat	0.14
	barley	0.29
	tomato	1.0

ANILINES (Plates 7.1–7.4)	Common Name	Approved Products
	dinitramine	Cobex
	trifluralin	Treflan, Tristar, Trident, Murphy Herbie
	pendimethalin	Stomp

The anilines are persistent soil-acting herbicides. Trifluralin can persist for more than six months; pendimethalin and dinitramine for about three and two months respectively. They stunt shoot growth with stunting and swelling of roots rather like the amides described in the previous section. Lateral roots are affected more than primary roots.

Examples are given below of crops damaged by residues of herbicide applied to a previous crop.

Herbicide	Crop	Residue in soil mg/kg
trifluralin	ryegrass	0.10
	oats	0.11
	wheat	0.16
	red beet	0.16

BENZONITRILES (Plates 8.1–8.4)	Common Name	Approved Products
	chlorthiamid	Prefix
	dichlobenil	Casoron G

Both herbicides in this group are soil-acting and very persistent. Chlorthiamid changes to dichlobenil in the soil in about three weeks. Dichlobenil is an inhibitor of actively growing meristems. The roots of damaged plants are stunted and thickened. The growing point is stunted and may be killed out. If applied too close to bushes or trees the bark at ground level may develop necrotic lesions. Dichlobenil is volatile and if used in or near glasshouses can cause serious damage to glasshouse crops.
   Dichlobenil degrades in the soil to dichlorbenzamide which can give marginal chlorosis of the leaves of fruit trees.

Examples are given below of crops damaged by residues of herbicide applied to a previous crop.

Herbicide	Crop	Residue in soil mg/kg
dichlobenil	carrot	0.05
	lettuce	0.12
	barley	0.17

CARBAMATES (Plates 9.1–9.2)	Common Name	Approved Products	Action
	barban*	Carbyne, Fisons B25	foliage
	chlorpropham*	Herbon CIPC 40%, Herbon Pabrac No. 2, MSS CIPC	soil
	phenmedipham	Betanal E	foliage
	propham*	Triherbide IPC	soil

* also occur in mixtures

The carbamates include herbicides which are mainly soil-acting and others whose action is predominantly through the foliage. They inhibit cell division and cause stunting with symptoms of damage similar to those of the amides described previously except for phenmedipham which also inhibits photosynthesis and causes chlorosis.

THIOCARBAMATES
(Plates 10.1–10.3)

Common Name	Approved products
cycloate	Ro-neet
di-allate	Avadex
EPTC	Eptam, Eradicane
tri-allate	Avadex BW

Thiocarbamates are soil-acting herbicides with persistence varying from about two to four months. They inhibit lipid synthesis within the plant. EPTC causes leaf cupping and necrosis of the tips. In plants damaged by di-allate, tri-allate or cycloate, young leaves stick to older leaves and in cereals this leads to a characteristic kinking near the base of the stem or near the seed. The moderate persistence of thiocarbamates rarely leads to residue problems but damage from misapplication may occur.

ETHOFUMESATE
(Plates 11.1–11.4)

Approved Product

Nortron

Although very different chemically ethofumesate affects plants in a similar manner to the thiocarbamates described in the previous section. It is soil-acting and persists for about four months.

ALIPHATIC ACIDS
(Plates 12.1–12.8)

Common Name	Approved Products
dalapon	Basfapon, BH Dalapon, Chafer Dalapon, Dow Dalapon, Dowpon, P P Dalapon, Synchemicals Dalapon
TCA	Actan, Hoechst NaTA, Tecane, Varitox

The aliphatic acids are inhibitors of lipid synthesis, like the thiocarbamates, but symptoms of damage are rather different. Sub-lethal doses reduce the amount of wax on the leaves, which can result in enhanced susceptibility to other foliage-acting herbicides. Damage causes an enhanced greenness, leaf cupping, general stunting and marginal necrosis.

Dalapon has a short persistence in the soil and its action is mainly foliar. TCA is predominantly soil-acting and can persist for up to about five months. Unlike most other herbicides, but like the growth regulators, they can be readily leached out of the soil by heavy rain.

GROWTH REGULATOR HERBICIDES
(Plates 13.1–13.20)

This group includes the following herbicides. Product names are not included because they are so numerous.

Benazolin, 2, 4–D, 2, 4–DB, dicamba, 3, 6–dichloropicolinic acid, dichlorprop, MCPA, MCPB, mecoprop (CMPP), picloram, 2, 4, 5–T, TBA.

This group of herbicides, often known as 'hormones', interferes with plant growth regulation. Symptoms of damage vary with dose, plant species and herbicides, the most common being leaf distortion with a tendency to parallel veining leading to the characteristic 'fern leaf' symptom. In brassicae, splitting of the stem usually occurs. Their action is mainly foliar but they can be absorbed from the soil. Persistence varies from more than two years for picloram, more than a year for TBA, to about two weeks for 2, 4–D.

DIFENZOQUAT
(Plates 14.1–14.3)

Approved Product

Avenge 630

Difenzoquat is a foliage-acting herbicide which is very specific to wild oats. Although it persists in the soil for some months it has almost no action through the soil at normal rates of application. Difenzoquat inhibits shoot growth leading to stunting and a gradual chlorosis. Tillering may be enhanced when damage occurs in wheat or barley. Damage after the tillering stage shortens the uppermost internode and the ear may be trapped in the leaf sheath.

BIPYRIDYLS
(Plates 15.1–15.7)

Common Name	Approved Products
diquat	Reglone
paraquat	Gramoxone

The bipyridyls are foliage-acting desiccants which destroy green tissue. They are completely inactivated by mineral soils but not completely inactivated by peaty soils. Uptake through the roots is possible in plants grown in sand or other soil-less culture and causes veinal chlorosis. If applied as a desiccant to potato haulm during drought conditions they can be translocated into the tuber causing vascular browning and stem end rotting.

BENTAZONE
(Plate 16.1)

Approved product

Basagran

Bentazone is a foliage-acting herbicide with short persistence in the soil. It causes stunting and scorch of the older leaves.

AMINOTRIAZOLE
(Plates 17.1–17.2)

Approved product

Weedazol. Occurs in several mixtures.

Aminotriazole is a soil-acting herbicide which persists for about a month. It causes severe chlorosis, usually bleaching and often with pink colorations, mainly on the younger leaves.

GLYPHOSATE
(Plates 18.1–18.2)

Approved Product

Roundup

Glyphosate is a foliage-acting herbicide which is inactivated by the soil. It causes chlorosis and stunting of the youngest leaves, often with distortion.

LIST OF COLOUR PLATES

Unless otherwise stated the symptoms were produced by uptake of the herbicide from the soil.

SUBSTITUTED UREAS	1.1	Linuron damage to potato (overdose)
	1.2	Metoxuron damage to barley (overdose)
	1.3	Chloroxuron damage to cucumber
	1.4	Linuron damage to carrot (overdose)
	1.5	Linuron damage to pea
	1.6	Chlorbromuron damage to French bean
	1.7	Diuron damage to blackcurrant (overdose)
	1.8	Chloroxuron damage to tomato
URACILS	2.1	Lenacil damage to cabbage
	2.2	Lenacil damage to strawberry (overdose)
	2.3	Terbacil damage to oat
	2.4	Terbacil damage to wheat
	2.5	Lenacil damage to chrysanthemum
	2.6	Lenacil damage to cucumber
	2.7	Bromacil damage to raspberry (overdose)
	2.8	Bromacil damage to French bean (affected and normal)
	2.9	Lenacil damage to sugar beet (normal and affected). 0 and 4 kg/ha pre emergence
TRIAZINES	3.1	Terbutryne with terbuthylazine damage to pea (overdose)
	3.2	Simazine damage to strawberry (overdose)
	3.3	Simazine damage to swede
	3.4	Simazine damage to French bean
	3.5	Atrazine damage to chrysanthemum
	3.6	Simazine damage to hop (overdose)
	3.7	Simazine damage to apple (overdose)
	3.8	Simazine damage to barley
	3.9	Cyanazine damage to potato
TRIAZINONES	4.1	Metribuzin damage to dwarf bean
	4.2	Metribuzin damage to barley
	4.3	Metribuzin damage to potato (overdose)
CHLORIDAZON	5.1	Chloridazon damage to sugar beet (normal and affected). 0 and 8 kg/ha pre-emergence
	5.2	Chloridazon damage to onion (normal and affected)
AMIDES	6.1	Butam damage to wheat (normal and affected)
	6.2	Propyzamide damage to hop (stunting and root thickening)
	6.3	Carbetamide damage to oilseed rape (overdose, affected and normal)
	6.4	Carbetamide damage to wheat
	6.5	Propyzamide damage to wheat
	6.6	Propyzamide damage to onion
	6.7	Propyzamide damage to carrot
	6.8	Propyzamide damage to strawberry (overdose)
	6.9	Propyzamide damage to cucumber

ANILINES	**7.1**	Trifluralin damage to wheat
	7.2	Trifluralin damage to runner bean (overdose)
	7.3	Trifluralin damage to onion
	7.4	Brussels sprouts 0,4 and 8 kg/ha trifluralin incorporated

BENZONITRILES	**8.1**	Dichlorbenzamide effect on apple
	8.2	Dichlobenil damage to French bean
	8.3	Dichlobenil damage to lettuce (normal and affected)
	8.4	Dichlobenil damage to wheat

| **CARBAMATES** | **9.1** | Barban damage to winter wheat |
| | **9.2** | Phenmedipham damage to sugar beet |

THIOCARBAMATES	**10.1**	Tri-allate damage to barley
	10.2	Tri-allate damage to wheat
	10.3	Tri-allate damage to sugar beet (leaf sticking)

ETHOFUMESATE	**11.1**	Ethofumesate damage to sugar beet (overdose)
	11.2	Ethofumesate damage to barley
	11.3	Ethofumesate damage to wheat
	11.4	Ethofumesate damage to potato

ALIPHATIC ACIDS	**12.1**	TCA damage to pea (reduction in leaf wax, normal and affected)
	12.2	TCA damage to cabbage (normal and affected)
	12.3	TCA damage to sugar beet
	12.4	Dalapon damage to tomato
	12.5	TCA damage to germinating wheat
	12.6	TCA damage to wheat (affected and normal)
	12.7	Dalapon residue damage to maize (normal and affected)
	12.8	Dalapon damage to French bean (affected and normal)

GROWTH REGULATOR HERBICIDES	**13.1**	TBA damage to potato (contaminated seed)
	13.2	TBA damage to lettuce
	13.3	Dichlorprop damage to lettuce (foliage application)
	13.4	MCPA damage to barley (foliage application too early)
	13.5	2, 4-D damage to tomato (foliage application)
	13.6	TBA damage to sugar beet (petiole fusion)
	13.7	Picloram damage to tomato
	13.8	2, 4–D damage to rose (spray drift)
	13.9	2, 4–D damage to blackcurrant (spray drift)
	13.10	Dicamba damage to apple (spray drift)
	13.11	TBA damage to French bean
	13.12	Mecoprop damage to oilseed rape (spray drift, flower abortion)
	13.13	Damage to wheat from dicamba, MCPA and mecroprop mixture (sprayed too late)
	13.14	TBA damage to tomato
	13.15	TBA damage to tomato
	13.16	3, 6–Dichloropicolinic acid damage to tomato
	13.17	3, 6–Dichloropicolinic acid damage to cucumber
	13.18	2, 4-D damage to tomato (foliage application)
	13.19	2, 4, 5–T damage to Brussels sprout (spray drift)
	13.20	Distortion and stem splitting in cucumber caused by foliage application of 2,4, 5–T

DIFENZOQUAT	**14.1**	Difenzoquat damage to wheat
	14.2	Difenzoquat damage to barley
	14.3	Difenzoquat damage to winter wheat (late application)

BIPYRIDYLS	**15.1**	Paraquat damage to tulip (applied previous autumn, translocated into bulb and then into flower)
	15.2	Paraquat damage to apple (spray drift)
	15.3	Paraquat damage to lettuce (spray drift)
	15.4	Paraquat damage to rhubarb (spray drift)
	15.5	Paraquat damage to alder bark (spray drift)
	15.6	Paraquat damage to potato (applied at emergence, translocated up shoot which later drops off)
	15.7	Diquat damage to potato (applied to haulm during drought)

| **BENTAZONE** | **16.1** | Bentazone damage to pea (foliage application, overdose) |

| **AMINOTRIAZOLE** | **17.1** | Aminotriazole damage to cabbage |
| | **17.2** | Aminotriazole damage to blackberry |

| **GLYPHOSATE** | **18.1** | Glyphosate damage to strawberry (spray drift) |
| | **18.2** | Glyphosate damage to tomato |

FIELD PATTERNS	**19.1**	Simazine damage to barley (headland overdosing in previous gooseberry crop)
	19.2	Propyzamide damage to strawberry (uneven application)
	19.3	Isoproturon damage to winter wheat (headland overlapping)

1.1 Linuron damage to potato (overdose)

1.2 Metoxuron damage to barley (overdose)

1.3 Chloroxuron damage to cucumber

1.4 Linuron damage to carrot (overdose)

1.5 Linuron damage to pea

1.6 Chlorbromuron damage to French bean

1.7 Diuron damage to blackcurrant (overdose)

1.8 Chloroxuron damage to tomato

2.1 Lenacil damage to cabbage

2.2 Lenacil damage to strawberry (overdose)

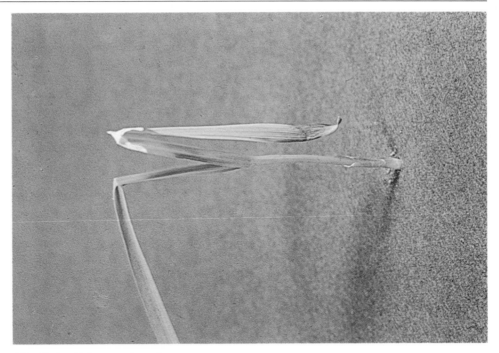

2.3 Terbacil damage to oat

2.4 Terbacil damage to wheat

2.5 Lenacil damage to chrysanthemum

2.6 Lenacil damage to cucumber

2.7 Bromacil damage to raspberry (overdose)

2.8 Bromacil damage to French bean (affected and normal)

2.9 Lenacil damage to sugar beet (normal and affected)

3.1 Terbutryne with terbuthylazine damage to pea (overdose)

3.2 Simazine damage to strawberry (overdose)

3.3 Simazine damage to swede

3.4 Simazine damage to French bean

3.5 Atrazine damage to chrysanthemum

3.6 Simazine damage to hop (overdose)

3.7 Simazine damage to apple (overdose)

3.8 Simazine damage to barley

3.9 Cyanazine damage to potato

4.1 Metribuzin damage to dwarf bean

4.2 Metribuzin damage to barley

4.3 Metribuzin damage to potato (overdose)

5.1 Chloridazon damage to sugar beet (normal and affected)

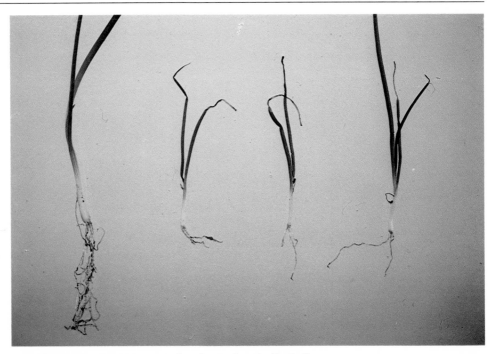

5.2 Chloridazon damage to onion (normal and affected)

AMIDES

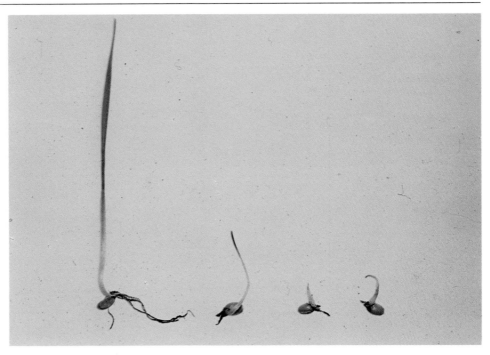

6.1 Butam damage to wheat (normal and affected)

6.2 Propoyzamide damage to hop

6.3 Carbetamide damage to oilseed rape (overdose, affected and normal)

6.4 Carbetamide damage to wheat

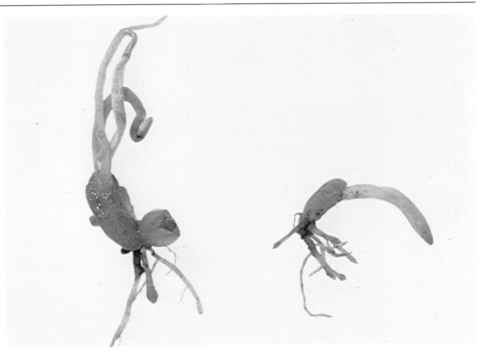

6.5 Propyzamide damage to wheat

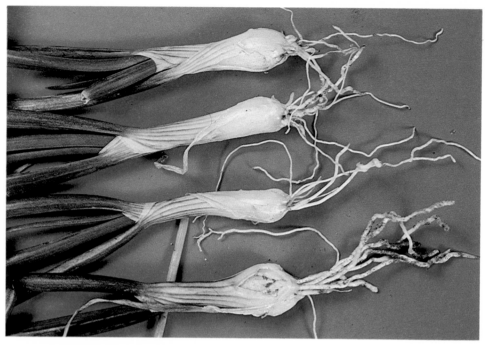

6.6 Propyzamide damage to onion

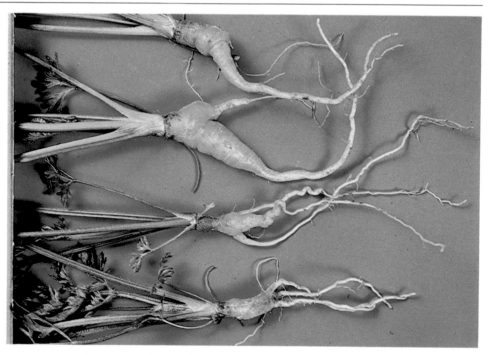

6.7 Propyzamide damage to carrot

6.8 Propyzamide damage to strawberry (overdose)

6.9 Propyzamide damage to cucumber

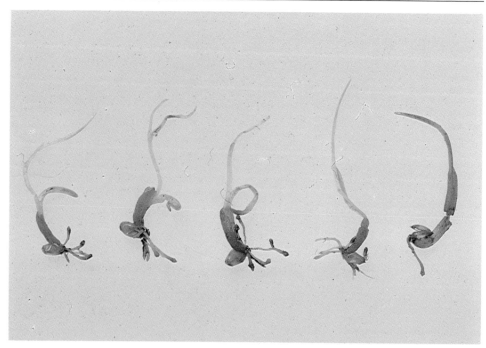

7.1   Trifluralin damage to wheat

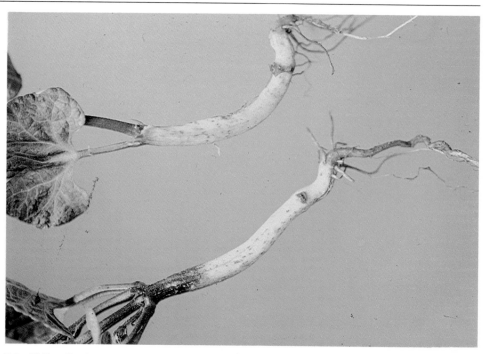

7.2   Trifluralin damage to runner bean (overdose)

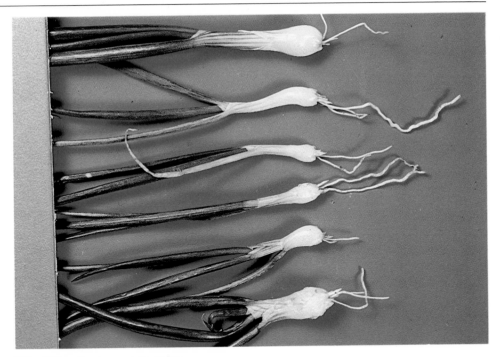

7.3 Trifluralin damage to onion

7.4 Trifluralin damage to Brussels sprout (normal and affected)

8.1   Dichlorbenzamide effect on apple

8.2   Dichlobenil damage to French bean

8.3 Dichlobenil damage to lettuce (normal and affected)

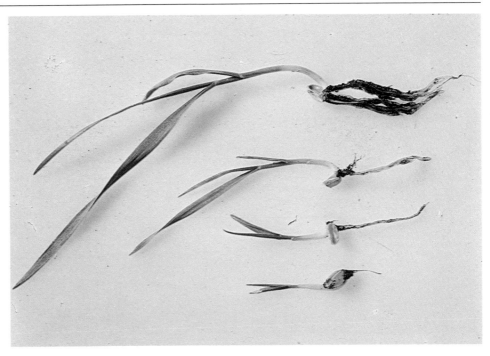

8.4 Dichlobenil damage to wheat

9.1 Barban damage to winter wheat

9.2 Phenmedipham damage to sugar beet

THIOCARBAMATES

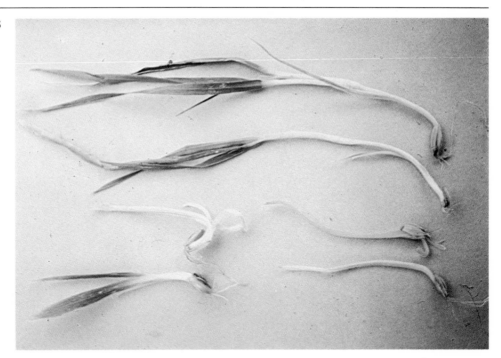

10.1 Tri-allate damage to barley

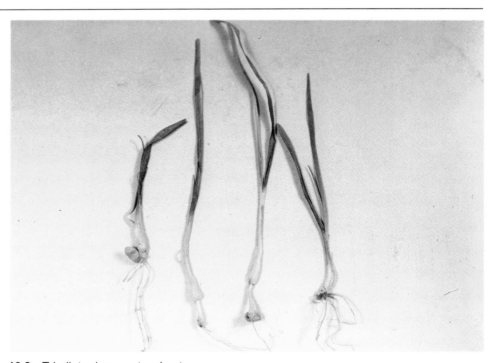

10.2 Tri-allate damage to wheat

10.3 Tri-allate damage to sugar beet (leaf sticking)

ETHOFUMESATE

11.1 Ethofumesate damage to sugar beet (overdose)

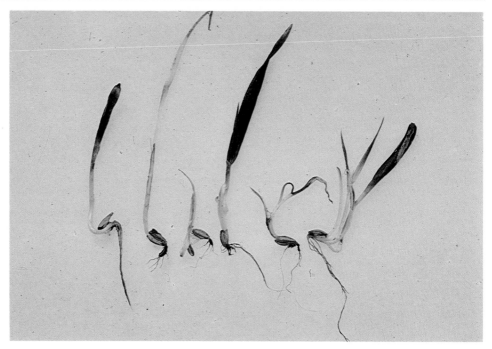

11.2 Ethofumesate damage to barley

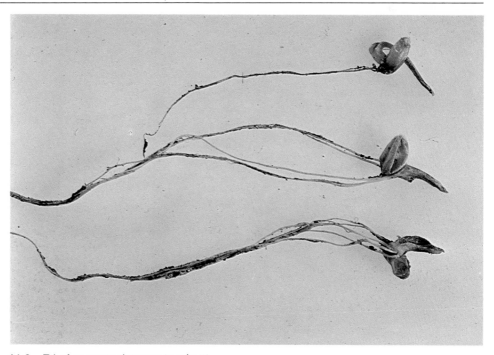

11.3 Ethofumesate damage to wheat

11.4 Ethofumesate damage to potato

12.1 TCA damage to pea (reduction in leaf wax, normal and affected)

12.2 TCA damage to cabbage (normal and affected)

12.3 TCA damage to sugar beet

12.4 Dalapon damage to tomato

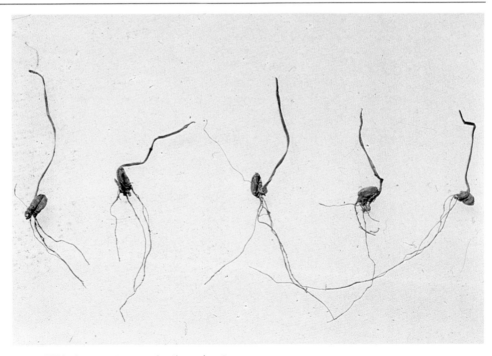

12.5 TCA damage to germinating wheat

12.6 TCA damage to wheat (affected and normal)

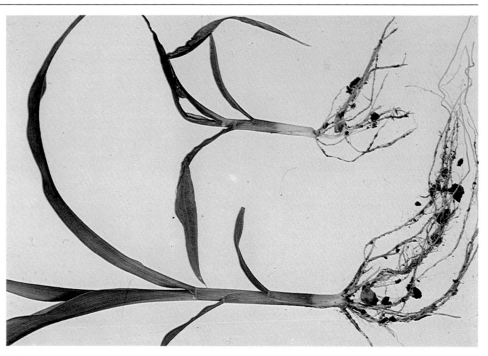

12.7 Dalapon residue damage to maize (normal and affected)

12.8 Dalapon damage to French bean (affected and normal)

13.1 TBA damage to potato (contaminated seed)

13.2 TBA damage to lettuce

13.3 Dichlorprop damage to lettuce (foliage application)

13.4 MCPA damage to barley (foliage application too early)

13.5 2, 4-D Damage to tomato (foliage application)

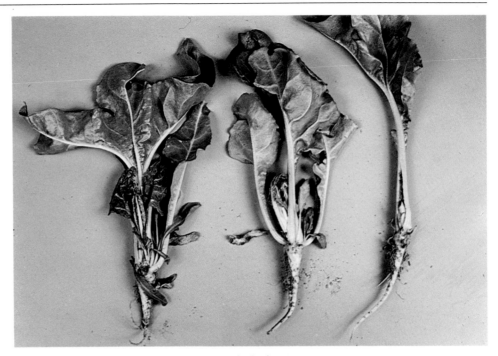

13.6 TBA damage to sugar beet (petiole fusion)

13.7 Picloram damage to tomato

13.8 2, 4-D damage to rose (spray drift)

13.9 2, 4-D damage to blackcurrant (spray drift)

13.10 Dicamba damage to apple (spray drift)

13.11 TBA damage to French bean

13.12 Mecoprop damage to oilseed rape (spray drift, flower abortion)

13.13 Damage to wheat from dicambra, MCPA and mecoprop mixture (sprayed too late)

13.14 TBA damage to tomato

13.15 TBA damage to tomato

13.16 3, 6-Dichloropicolinic acid damage to tomato

13.17 3, 6-Dichloropicolinic acid damage to cucumber

13.18 2, 4-D damage to tomato (foliage application)

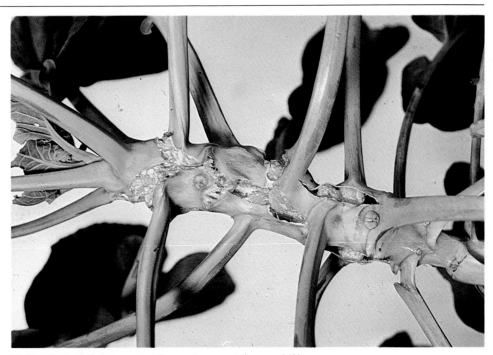

13.19 2, 4, 5-T damage to Brussels sprout (spray drift)

13.20 2, 4, 5-T damage to cucumber (foliage application)

DIFENZOQUAT

14.1 Difenzoquat damage to wheat

14.2 Difenzoquat damage to barley

14.3 Difenzoquat damage to winter wheat (late application)

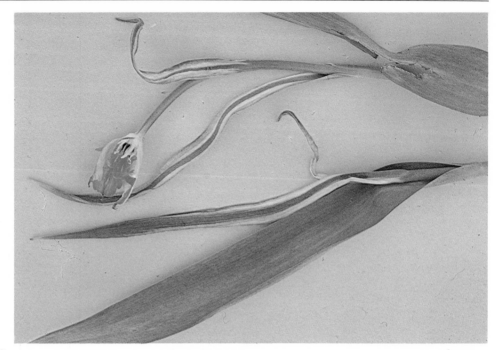

15.1 Paraquat damage to tulip (applied previous autumn, translocated into bulb and then into flower)

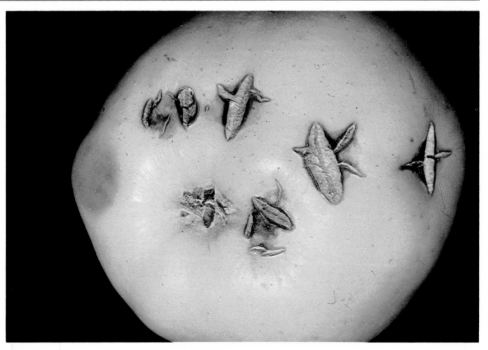

15.2 Paraquat damage to apple (spray drift)

15.3 Paraquat damage to lettuce (spray drift)

15.4 Paraquat damage to rhubarb (spray drift)

15.5 Paraquat damage to alder bark (spray drift)

15.6 Paraquat damage to potato (applied at emergence, translocated up shoot which later drops off)

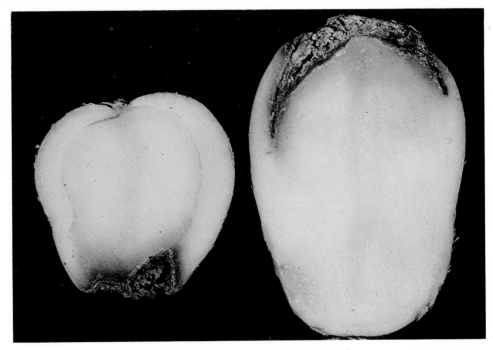

15.7 Diquat damage to potato (applied to haulm during drought)

BENTAZONE

16.1 Bentazone damage to pea (foliage application, overdose)

17.1 Aminotriazole damage to cabbage

17.2 Aminotriazole damage to blackberry

GLYPHOSATE

18.1 Glyphosate damage to strawberry (spray drift)

18.2 Glyphosate damage to tomato

19.1 Simazine damage to barley (headland overdosing in previous gooseberry crop)

19.2 Propyzamide damage to strawberry (uneven application)

19.3 Isoproturon damage to winter wheat (headland overlapping)

Printed in England for Her Majesty's Stationery Office
by Linneys of Mansfield
Dd 696924   C80   12/80